THE PUFFALUMPS'
Pillow Poems

selected by Emily George
illustrated by Kristin Johnson

MARVEL BOOKS

The Puffalumps and the Puffalump characters are trademarks of Fisher-Price division of
The Quaker Oats Company. Copyright © 1987 Fisher-Price. All rights reserved. Program created
by Parachute Press, Inc. Published by Marvel Books, a New World Pictures Company.
387 Park Avenue South, New York, NY 10016. Printed in the U.S.A. ISBN 0-87135-242-7

Puffalump Time

We are bouncing.
    We are flying.
        We are floating on the air!
The Puffalumps are coming
    With pillow poems to share.

Are you wearing your pajamas?
Have you put your toys away?
Did you scrub-a-dub-dub-dubble
In the bathtub yet today?

Are you ready for a snuggle?
    Are you ready for a rhyme?
        Are you comfy?
            Are you cozy?
Then it's Puffalump time!
                    —The Puffalumps

Summer Treat

Between supper time and bedtime
Rolling slowly through the streets,
Comes a bright white ice-cream wagon
Packed with ice-cold ice-cream treats.

When they hear that jingle-jangle
Children run from far and wide,
And their tummies all are ready
To put something good inside!

—Emily George

Bed in Summer

In winter I get up at night
And dress by yellow candle-light.
In summer, quite the other way,
I have to go to bed by day.

I have to go to bed and see
The birds still hopping on the tree,
Or hear the grown-up people's feet
Still going past me in the street.

And does it not seem hard to you,
When all the sky is clear and blue,
And I should like so much to play,
To have to go to bed by day?

—Robert Louis Stevenson

Swimming

Watch me swim!
I lie down so

And make my hands
And both feet go;

I blow to keep
The water away;

And breathe with ease
In the proper way.

I can swim fine
As fine can be

So long as I
Keep out of the sea.
—*Alice Higgins*

Child's Evening Hymn

Day is over,
Night draws high,
Shadows of the evening
Steal across the sky.

Darkness gathers,
Stars begin to peep;
Birds and beasts and flowers
Soon will be asleep.
—*Sabine Baring-Gould*

Go to Bed First

Go to bed first,
A golden purse;
Go to bed second,
A golden pheasant;
Go to bed third,
A golden bird.
                    —*Anonymous*

Advice

Go to bed late,
Stay very small;
Go to bed early,
Grow very tall.
—*Mother Goose*

More Advice

The cock crows in the morn
To tell us to rise,
And he that lies late
Will never be wise.

For early to bed
And early to rise
Is the way to be healthy
And wealthy and wise.
—*Mother Goose*

The Man in the Moon

The Man in the Moon looked out of the moon,
Looked out of the moon and said,
"'Tis time for all children on the earth
To think about getting to bed!"

—*Mother Goose*

The Evening Is Coming

The evening is coming.
The sun sinks to rest.
The birds are all flying
Straight home to their nests.
"Caw, caw," says the crow
As he flies overhead.
It's time little children
Were going to bed.

Here comes the pony.
His work is all done.
Down through the meadow
He takes a good run.
Up go his heels,
And down goes his head.
It's time little children
Were going to bed.
            —*Thomas Hood*

The Star

Twinkle, twinkle, little star,
How I wonder what you are!
Up above the world so high,
Like a diamond in the sky.

As your bright and tiny spark,
Lights the traveler in the dark—
Though I know not what you are,
Twinkle, twinkle, little star.

—*Jane Taylor*

The Moon

I see the moon,
And the moon sees me,
And the moon sees somebody
I want to see.
God bless the moon,
And God bless me,
And God bless the somebody
I want to see.

—Anonymous

Boys and Girls, Come Out to Play

Boys and girls, come out to play!
The moon is shining, bright as day.
Leave your supper and leave your sleep,
And meet your playmates in the street;
Come with a whoop and come with a call.
Come with goodwill or don't come at all.
Up the ladder and down the wall,
A batch of cookies will serve us all.
You find sugar; I'll find flour,
And we'll have a party in half an hour.

—Mother Goose

Excuses, Excuses

I'm just not ready for bedtime.
I must give dolly a drink,
And my things keep disappearing
So I have to stop and think.

Where did I put my pajamas?
Where did my slippers go?
Did they take a walk without me?
Please tell me if you know.
—*Emily George*

Willie Winkie

Wee Willie Winkie runs through the town,
Upstairs and downstairs in his nightgown,
Rapping at the window, crying through the lock,
Are the children all in bed, for now it's eight o'clock?
—Mother Goose

The Lullaby Lady

Have you heard of the Lullaby Lady,
Who lives on a cloud, snowy white;
Where she sits making songs for the children,
By the rays of the moon, all the night?

—*Loryn Parker*

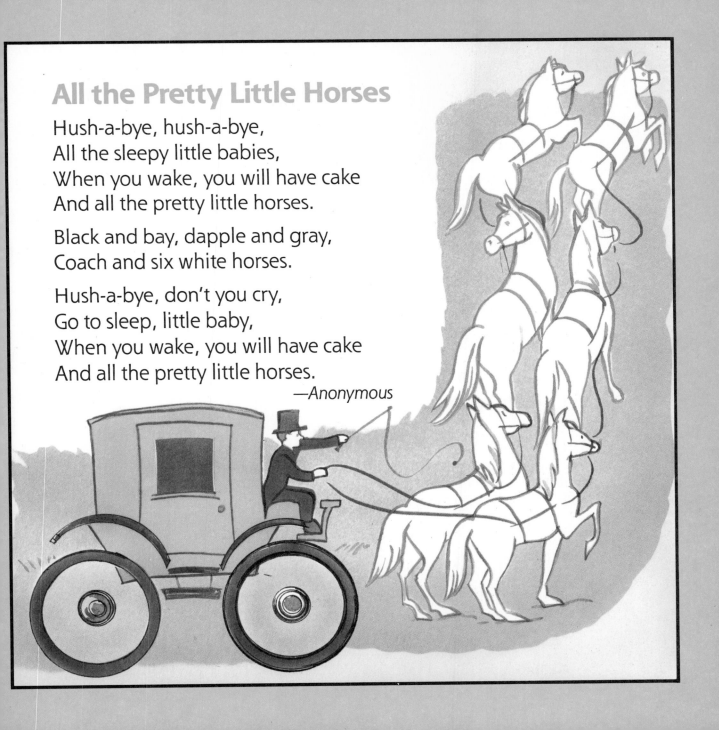

All the Pretty Little Horses

Hush-a-bye, hush-a-bye,
All the sleepy little babies,
When you wake, you will have cake
And all the pretty little horses.

Black and bay, dapple and gray,
Coach and six white horses.

Hush-a-bye, don't you cry,
Go to sleep, little baby,
When you wake, you will have cake
And all the pretty little horses.

—*Anonymous*

Hush, Little Baby

Hush, little baby, don't say a word,
Mama's going to buy you a mockingbird.

And if that mockingbird don't sing,
Mama's going to buy you a diamond ring.

And if that diamond ring turns brass,
Mama's going to buy you a looking glass.

And if that looking glass gets broke,
Mama's going to buy you a billy goat.

And if that billy goat won't pull,
Mama's going to buy you a cart and bull.

And if that cart and bull turn over,
Mama's going to buy you a dog named Rover.

And if that dog named Rover won't bark,
Mama's going to buy you a horse and cart.

And if that horse and cart fall down,
You'll still be the sweetest little baby in town.

—*Anonymous*

Diddle, Diddle, Dumpling

Diddle, diddle, dumpling,
My son John,
Went to bed
With his trousers on;
One shoe off,
And one shoe on,
Diddle, diddle, dumpling,
My son John.

—*Mother Goose*

Two by Two

Please tuck me into bed with you.
Let's go to dreamland, two by two.
Tomorrow is another day
With time to talk and time to play.
But now it's best we both should rest—
Two little birds in one snug nest.

—Puffalump Bear

The Land of Nod

From breakfast on through all the day
At home among my friends I stay;
But every night I go abroad
Afar into the land of Nod.

All by myself I have to go.
With none to tell me what to do—
All alone beside the streams
And up the mountain-sides of dreams.

The strangest things are there for me,
Both things to eat and things to see,
And many frightening sights abroad
Till morning in the land of Nod.

Try as I like to find the way,
I never can get back by day,
Nor can remember plain and clear
The curious music that I hear.

—*Robert Louis Stevenson*

Dreamland

There are no rules in dreamland,
Nor does it stay the same.
You might meet people whom you know
Or creatures you can't name.
You might ride flying zebras
And do amazing things
Like leaping over castle walls
To play croquet with kings!
You might be in a meadow
That's blanketed with snow
And pick bouquets of bluebells
Which nod and say "hello."
You might be at the seashore
With a mermaid and a seal
Or with elves in a forest
Who seem completely real.
You might be in a jungle
Where birds have music schools.
When you visit dreamland,
You won't find *any* rules!

—*Bobbi Katz*

Morning Song

Donkey, donkey, old and gray,
Open your mouth and gently bray;
Lift your ears and blow your horn,
To wake the world this sleepy morn.
—*Mother Goose*